C000182834

This is a Parragon Book.

© Parragon 1997.

Parragon
13-17 Avonbridge Trading Estate
Atlantic Road, Avonmouth
Bristol, BS11 9QD

Produced by The Templar Company plc,
Pippbrook Mill, London Road, Dorking,
Surrey RH4 1JE

Written by Robert Snedden
Series Designer Mark Summersby

All photographs copyright © TRH pictures,
255-257 Liverpool Rd, London N1 1LX
except for page 19, courtesy of Boeing/Sikorsky
and page 69, courtesy of Mitsubishi Heavy Industries.

Printed and bound in the UK

ISBN 0 7525 1689 2

FACTFINDERS

MODERN COMBAT
AIRCRAFT

PARRAGON

CONTENTS

In 1909, the first military aircraft in history was delivered to the US Signal Corps. Like the original Wright brothers' flying machine, it had the engine behind the pilot and in front of the propellers. It had a 30-horse-power engine, skids for landing and a two-man crew. It was launched from a monorail catapult and had a top speed of 68km/h (42.5mph). It could stay in the air for an hour. It cost $25,000. Compare that to the F-15 Strike Eagle, which can fly at over 2500km/h, has a range of over 4500km and carries a bewildering and deadly array of weapons. Each one costs $30,000,000.

Many advances have been made in armament design since World War I, when the state-of-the-art technology was a synchronised machine-gun, fired between the blades of the propeller. Today's fighters may have 20-mm automatic multi-barrel guns firing up to 6,000 rounds a minute. For air-to-air combat they carry guided missiles such as the Sidewinder, Phoenix or Sparrow. Operating against ground targets, they carry high-explosive or nuclear bombs, rockets and various types of guided bombs and missiles.

In the early days of flying the military student pilot was often self-taught. First he would become familiar with the use and feel of the controls on the ground. Then he would practice taxiing. Having mastered this, he would take off and fly for short distances, gradually lengthening the flights until he was confident he could fly solo. Today's pilots spend over a year in study and training with many hours in flight simulators. Many military test pilots have degrees in engineering.

The tremendous progress made in aircraft technology has had a major effect on the tasks of the pilot. Much of the routine work of flying the aircraft is done by the automatic pilot, and navigation can also be performed by on-board systems. Terrain-following radar can fly the aircraft safely at extremely low altitudes; automatic landing systems can land a plane safely under a cloud ceiling of less than 30m (100ft) and with less than 1km visibility. Automatic systems using optical, infra-red and radar guide some munitions, so that they can be delivered with greater accuracy than was possible before, even from considerable distances.

Automatic systems enable the crew to perform missions that formerly required many more men. The pilot's job is that of monitoring the instruments and automatic control systems, taking over from them in case of emergency. However, in all military missions the pilot and other crew members are required to perform crucial tasks such as detecting and identifying the target, discriminating between real and false targets and between friend and foe, and deciding when and how to attack. In air-to-air combat the pilot needs to have skill, judgement, endurance, keen vision, a fine sense of timing and spatial relationships, to say nothing of courage and aggression.

BELL SUPERCOBRA

Type:	two-man helicopter gunship
Engines:	two 1723hp General Electric T700-GE-401 turboshafts
Wingspan:	3.28m (10ft 9in)
Length:	17.68m (58ft)
Height:	4.44m (14ft 7in)
Weight:	4634kg (10,216lb) empty; 6690kg (14,750lb) maximum take-off weight
Maximum speed:	352km/h (219mph); 282km/h (175mph) at sea level
Service ceiling:	4270m (14,000ft)
Maximum range:	635km (340 miles)
Armament:	one undernose M197 3-barrel 20mm gun and up to 1119kg (2466lb) of anti-tank guided missiles, bombs or anti-aircraft missiles
First flight:	16 November 1983 (twin-engine model)

The Bell AH-1W SuperCobra, operated by the US
Marine Corps, is an upgrade of the AH-1T Improved
SeaCobra, itself developed from the AH-1 HueyCobra,
flown by the US Army. Improvements over the earlier
models included a longer fuselage with self-sealing,
damage-resistant rubber cells, resistant to the impact of
12mm calibre weapons, carrying extra fuel. The
SuperCobra is powered by twin turboshaft engines,
mounted either side of the upper mid-fuselage. The
two-man crew of the helicopter are protected by extra
armour in the fuselage. The cockpit is equipped with dual
controls and a head-up display that can be used in
conjunction with night vision goggles. A modified
version of the SuperCobra, called the Venom, may be
acquired by the British Army.

BAe Harrier GR.7

Type:	VTOL single-seat fighter-bomber
Engines:	one 96.75kN Rolls Royce Pegasus Mk 105 turbofan
Wingspan:	9.25m (30ft 4in)
Length:	14.36m (37ft 2in)
Height:	3.55m (11ft 8in)
Weight:	7050kg (15,542lb) empty; 14,061kg (31,000lb) maximum short take-off weight; 8505kg (18,950lb) vertical take-off weight
Maximum speed:	967km/h (601mph) at sea level; 1065km/h (661mph) on take-off run
Service ceiling:	15,200m (50,000ft)
Maximum range:	740km (400 miles)
Armament:	two Aden 25mm revolver cannon, up to 4173kg (9200lb) of bombs, 68mm rocket pods and anti-aircraft missiles
First flight:	9 November 1978 (Harrier II)

The British Aerospace Harrier GR.7 is the latest in a line of combat-proven aircraft. This is the night-attack variant of an aircraft which was in fact produced as a joint venture with McDonnell Douglas of the USA. Initially produced for the US Marine Corps, the new aircraft was acquired by the RAF in 1987 and designated the Harrier GR.5. All of these aircraft were upgraded to GR.7s by the end of 1994. The GR.7 has a longer fuselage and larger wing area than earlier versions of the Harrier. Equipment for the night-attack role includes a digital moving map display, head-up display and night vision goggles. Forward-looking infra-red and laser seeking and targetting systems ensure accurate weapons delivery. The Harrier is also equipped with electronic counter measures and flare dispensers for self-defence.

BAe Sea Harrier FRS.1

Type:	single-seat multi-role combat aircraft
Engines:	96.5kN Rolls-Royce Pegasus Mk 104 vectored thrust turbofan
Wingspan:	7.70m (25ft 3in)
Length:	14.50m (47ft 7in)
Height:	3.71m (12ft 2in)
Weight:	6374kg (14,052lb) empty; 11,880kg (26,200lb) maximum take-off weight
Maximum speed:	1185km/h (736mph) at low level
Service ceiling:	15,600m (51,000ft)
Maximum range:	750km (460 miles)
Armament:	two optional 30mm Aden gun pods, up to 3630kg (8000lb) of WE177 nuclear bombs, Sea Eagle air-to-ship missiles, AIM anti-aircraft missiles
First flight:	20 August 1978

The British Aerospace Sea Harrier FRS.1 was based on the Harrier GR.3 designed for the Royal Air Force. The improvements included a raised seat for the pilot, mounted in a repositioned cockpit to improve visibility. Additionally, room was made for air-to-air and air-to-ground radar in the nose and an improved navigational and attack system in the cockpit. All components that could have been damaged by contact with seawater were replaced. In 1982, the FRS.1 saw combat duty in the Falklands campaign. Flying over 2000 sorties, the 29 Sea Harriers shot down 22 Argentine aircraft for the loss in combat of only four of their number. The FRS.1s are currently being upgraded to F/A.2s with improved radar systems capable of multiple targetting and with longer range air-to-air missiles, greatly improving the FRS.1s already impressive combat capability.

BOEING RAH-66 COMANCHE

Type:	two-seat armed reconnaissance helicopter
Engines:	two 1002kW LHTEC T800-LHT-801 turboshafts
Rotor diameter:	11.90m (39ft)
Length:	14.28m (46ft 10in), including rotor turning circle
Height:	3.39m (11ft 2in)
Weight:	3515kg (7749lb) empty; 4587kg (10,112lb) loaded
Maximum speed:	328km/h (204mph) maximum level speed
Service ceiling:	not known
Maximum range:	2335km (1260 nautical miles)
Armament:	one 20mm cannon, 10 Hellfire anti-tank guided missiles, 14 Stinger anti-aircraft missiles
First flight:	4 January 1996

The joint Boeing/Sikorsky RAH-66 Comanche was selected in the 1980s when rival manufacturers competed to design a helicopter to replace a number of ageing models currently in service with the US Army. The two-man crew sit in tandem, with the pilot in front and the weapons officer behind him, in contrast to most other attack helicopters where the seating arrangement is reversed. The Comanche is capable of night attack, employing its front-looking infra-red system and laser targetting to do so. Side-opening weapons bays situated behind the main undercarriage can each house six anti-aircraft missiles or three Hellfire anti-tank guided missiles. Additional missiles can be mounted on removable stub wings. Auxiliary fuel tanks can also be carried to increase the Comanche's operational range. Production should begin in 2001.

MIRAGE 2000

Type:	two-seat combat aircraft
Engines:	one 95.1kN SNECMA M53-P2 turbofan
Wingspan:	9.13m (29ft 2in)
Length:	14.36m (47ft 1in)
Height:	5.20m (17ft)
Weight:	7500kg (16,534lb) empty; 17,000kg (37,480lb) maximum take-off weight
Maximum speed:	2338km/h (1453mph) level speed
Service ceiling:	18,500m (60,000ft)
Maximum range:	1300km (780 nautical miles) (combat range)
Armament:	two DEFA 554 30mm cannon; up to 6300kg (13,889lb) of bombs and missiles, including laser-guided bombs, anti-runway bombs, anti-aircraft and anti-radiation missiles
First flight:	10 March 1978

The Dassault Mirage 2000 is the main combat aircraft of the French Air Force for the beginning of the 21st century. It is a highly manoeuvrable and agile aircraft, aided by a fly-by-wire flight control system and excellent handling. First deliveries were of the 2000C, the interceptor version. In the early 1990s the upgraded Mirage 2000-5 was introduced with an improved powerplant and the ability to carry the powerful Skyflash anti-aircraft missiles. Two-seat trainer and single-seat reconnaissance version have also been produced. The Mirage 2000N, based on the two-seat trainer, was designed as a nuclear bomber. Designed to fly low-level attack missions, the 2000N has a specially strengthened fuselage and a terrain-following radar system that allows it to fly 60 metres above the ground at speeds in excess of 1000km/h.

MIRAGE RAFALE

Type: one/two seat multi-role combat aircraft

Engines: two SNECMA M88-3 afterburning turbofans

Wingspan: 10.9m (35ft 9in)

Length: 15.3m (50ft 2in)

Height: 5.34m (17ft 6in)

Weight: 10,000kg (22,026lb) empty; 22,500kg (49,560lb) loaded

Maximum speed: 1390km/h (864mph) at low level
2125km/h (1321mph) at 11,000m

Service ceiling: not known

Maximum range: 1850km (1150 miles)

Armament: one GIAT DEFA 30mm cannon plus 6000kg (13,228lb) external ordnance, including tactical nuclear missile, bombs and fuel tanks

First flight: 19 May 1991

The Dassault Rafale was designed as a new generation multi-role combat aircraft for the French air force and navy. The single-seat Rafale C is the version chosen for the air force. It is an exceedingly versatile aircraft, equipped with no less than 14 hardpoints for the mounting of a wide range of ordnance, including stand-off nuclear missiles. The navy version, the Rafale M, is a heavier aircraft and is equipped with an arrestor hook for landing on aircraft carriers. It has one less hardpoint than the Rafale C. A third version, the Rafale B, was originally intended for a role as a dual control trainer, but is being developed for a fully operational role. All three are equipped with the same weapons, navigation systems and engines. Deliveries of the Rafale are scheduled to begin in 1998 and continue until 2009.

EUROCOPTER AS565 PANTHER

Type:	two-seat multi-role helicopter (statistics are for the submarine assault variant)
Engines:	two Turbomeca Arriel IM1 turboshafts
Rotor diameter:	11.94m (39ft 2in)
Length:	12.11m (39ft 9in) (fuselage)
Height:	3.99m (13ft 1in)
Weight:	2262kg (4987lb) empty; 4250kg (9370lb) maximum take-off weight
Maximum speed:	296km/h (184mph)
Service ceiling:	2600m (8350ft)
Maximum range:	850km (530 miles
Armament:	four anti-submarine missiles or two homing torpedoes
First flight:	29 February 1984

The joint French and German designed Eurocopter AS
565 Panther is available in a number of variants, in
service with all branches of the armed services. In its
army role, an early model was designed as an unarmed
fast troop transport, carrying up to 10 men in the cabin.
A later model added outriggers to the fuselage for a
choice of ordnance, including gunpods or air-to-air
missiles. An anti-tank variant of the Panther is equipped
with a roof mounted sight and anti-tank guided missiles
developed by Euromissile. Navy versions of the Panther
can also be armed or unarmed, unarmed models being
employed for surveillance and sea-air rescue missions.
Attack versions are equipped for anti-ship missions or for
anti-submarine sorties. The anti-submarine Panther
carries two homing torpedoes and is equipped with a
magnetic anomaly detector for acquiring the target.

EUROCOPTER TIGER

Type:	two-seat attack helicopter
Engines:	two MTU/Rolls-Royce Turbomeca MTR 390 turboshafts
Rotor diameter:	13m (42ft 8in)
Length:	14m (45ft 1in)
Height:	4.32m (14ft 2in)
Weight:	3300kg (7275lb) empty; 6000kg (13,227lb) maximum take-off weight
Maximum speed:	280km/h (174mph)
Service ceiling:	2000m (6500ft)
Maximum range:	1300km (700 miles)
Armament:	30mm cannon, four anti-aircraft missiles, two 22-round 68mm rocket pods, two 12-round rocket pods
First flight:	27 April 1991

Like the Eurocopter Panther, the Eurocopter Tiger, or Tigre, is a joint French and German production, specifically designed for anti-tank missions. The two-man crew are seated with the co-pilot/gunner in the forward cockpit above the nose and the pilot in a raised rear cockpit behind him. In addition to its eight anti-tank missiles, the Tiger can carry four anti-aircraft missiles. The Tigre HAP, designed to perform a close support role with the French army, will be equipped with a 30mm cannon, armour-piercing rockets and air-to-air missiles, among other weapons. Target acquisition will be by forward-looking infra-red, laser rangefinding and a roof-mounted TV sight. It is expected that the first deliveries of this formidably armed machine will be made to the French army in 1999.

EUROFIGHTER 2000

Type:	single-seat air defence fighter
Engines:	two Eurojet EJ200 afterburning turbofans
Wingspan:	10.5m (34ft 5in)
Length:	14.5m (47ft 7in)
Height:	6.4m (21ft)
Weight:	9750kg (21,495lb) empty; 21,000kg (46,297lb) maximum take-off weight
Maximum speed:	2125km/h (1321mph)
Service ceiling:	not known
Maximum range:	550km (345 miles) combat radius
Armament:	one 27mm cannon, up to 6500kg assorted ordnance, including anti-air-craft missiles, surface-to-air missiles and auxiliary fuel tanks
First flight:	29 March 1994

The Eurofighter 2000 is being jointly developed by
Germany, Italy, Great Britain and Spain. To date the
project has been plagued by political infighting, which
has delayed production of the aircraft. France, originally
involved in the project, withdrew to concentrate on
their own Rafale. Following insistence by the German
partners that a cheaper version of the proposed aircraft
be found, the project was relaunched in 1992. Seven
aircraft are being built for the test programme. The
Eurofighter is a single-seat air defence and air
superiority fighter that can be equipped for a secondary
role as a ground attack aircraft. Fitted with a
sophisticated fly-by-wire system, the Eurofighter should
be a highly manoeuvrable aircraft. Multi-mode radar
systems will allow it to acquire and track several
targets simultaneously.

FAIRCHILD A10A THUNDERBOLT

Type:	single-seat close support aircraft
Engines:	two General Electric TF34-GE-100 turbofans
Wingspan:	17.53m (57ft 6in)
Length:	16.26m (53ft 4in)
Height:	4.47m (14ft 8in)
Weight:	11,321kg (24,959lb) empty; 22,680kg (50,000lb) maximum take-off weight
Maximum speed:	706km/h (439mph)
Service ceiling:	13,700m (45,000ft)
Maximum range:	4000km (2200 miles)
Armament:	one 30mm cannon and up to 7258kg (16,000lb) assorted ordnance, including air-to-ground missiles, laser-guided bombs and air-to-air missiles
First flight:	10 May 1972

The Fairchild A10A Thunderbolt, nicknamed the 'Warthog', was one of the most important air weapons of the Coalition Forces during the Gulf War in 1990-91. The Warthog provides close support for ground troops and a deadly anti-tank capability. Its armament is fearsome, including a seven-barrel rotating cannon that is capable of firing 30mm shells at up to 4200 rounds per minute. Laser targetting technology helps the pilot to stay on target. The Warthog is designed for battlefield survival. Its wings are designed to give high manoeuvrability at low speeds and the engine pods are housed towards the rear of the aircraft. The pilot is protected by titanium armour plating, which also protects the ammunition belts for the rotary cannon. Recent improvements to the aircraft have included making the cannon capable of air-to-air targetting as well as air-to-ground.

GENERAL DYNAMICS F-111

Type:	all-weather attack aircraft
Engines:	two Pratt and Whitney TF30 after-burning turbofans
Wingspan:	19.2m (63ft) spread; 9.74m (32ft) swept
Length:	22.4m (73ft 6in)
Height:	5.22m (17ft 1in)
Weight:	21,537kg (47,481lb) empty; 45,360kg (100,000lb) fully loaded
Maximum speed:	2655km/h (1650mph)
Service ceiling:	18,300m (60,000ft) at combat weight
Maximum range:	4700km (2540 miles) maximum internal fuel
Armament:	nuclear weapons in internal bay; one 20mm M61 cannon, six underwing pylons for laser-guided bombs, missiles
First flight:	21 December 1964

The General Dynamics F-111 was developed in the 1960s
to answer the US Navy's requirement for a long-range
interceptor, and that of the US Air Force for a
deep-strike interdictor. It was the first aircraft to feature
a variable geometry 'swingwing' configuration. To begin
with, the F-111's performance was disappointing. It was
found to be too heavy for carrier-borne operations and in
combat over Vietnam suffered an unacceptable loss rate.
Improvements were subsequently made to the
specifications and the F-111 developed a role as a
strategic bomber capable of accurate delivery of its
payload. The final variant to be produced was the F-111F
with the ability to employ laser-guided weapons and
equipped with more reliable engines. Because of its
long upturned nose the F-111 has been nicknamed
the Aardvark.

GENERAL DYNAMICS F-16

Type:	multi-role single-seat fighter-bomber
Engines:	General Electric F110-GE-129 turbofan
Wingspan:	9.45m (31ft)
Length:	15.03m (49ft 4in)
Height:	5.09m (16ft 8in)
Weight:	7390kg (16,292lb) empty; 17,010kg (37,500lb) maximum take-off weight (F-16A)
Maximum speed:	2124km/h (1320mph)
Service ceiling:	15,240m (50,000ft)
Maximum range:	797km (430 miles) with four bombs and centre tank
Armament:	one M61-A1 20mm gun, centre pylon for drop tank or 1000kg (2200lb) bomb, wing pylons for 1700kg (3750lb) assorted bombs
First flight:	2 February 1974 (prototype)

The General Dynamics F-16 Fighting Falcon is one of the world's foremost fighting aircraft. The important features of the Fighting Falcon are its excellent performance in climbing and turning flight, a consequence of high powered engines, fly-by-wire control system, giving high agility, and a bubble canopy offering an unrivalled field of vision for the pilot, who sits in a semi-reclined position. The advanced electronic systems allow the pilot to acquire and track several targets simultaneously at long range in any weather conditions and accurately bomb targets in poor visibility. The F-16's combat range exceeds that of all potential enemy fighter aircraft. It also has a warning system and electronic counter measure pods to be used against airborne or surface electronic threats, making it a formidable target for anyone to take on.

GRUMMAN F-14 TOMCAT

Type:	two-seat carrier-based interceptor
Engines:	two General Electric F110-400 after-burning turbofans
Wingspan:	19.52m (64ft 2in) spread; 11.60m (38ft 2in) swept
Length:	18.87m (61ft 11in)
Height:	4.88m (16ft)
Weight:	18,110kg (39,921lb) empty; 33,724kg (74,349lb) fully loaded
Maximum speed:	2517km/h (1564mph)
Service ceiling:	17,000m (56,000ft)
Maximum range:	400km (217 miles) interception radius at Mach 1.5
Armament:	one 20mm M61 cannon, plus up to eight air-to-air missiles
First flight:	29 September 1986 (F-14A+)

The Grumman F-14 Tomcat has, with some justification, been described as the greatest long-range interceptor in the world. It was the alternative fighter designed by Grumman when the F-111 proved to be too heavy for carrier deployment. Grumman used the experience of developing the F-111 in producing a swingwing aircraft in the design of the Tomcat. The first of the US Navy's Tomcats were delivered in 1972 and it remains today one of the most formidable aircraft flying. Equipped with Phoenix air-to-air missiles and a sophisticated radar and fire-control system, the Tomcat can acquire, track and, if necessary, destroy six targets simultaneously at a range in excess of 160km (100 miles). An array of other weaponry also allows it to take on targets at closer range.

KAMOV KA50 WEREWOLF

Type:	single-seat close support helicopter
Engines:	two 1633kW Klimov TV3-117VK turboshafts
Rotor diameter:	14.5m (47ft 7in)
Length:	13.5m (44ft 3in) (fuselage)
Height:	4.93m (16ft 2in)
Weight:	9800kg (21,605lb) normal take-off weight; 10,800kg (23,810lb) maximum take-off weight
Maximum speed:	310km/h (193mph) in level flight
Service ceiling:	4000m (13,125ft)
Maximum range:	250km (155 miles)
Armament:	one 30mm cannon, four 80mm unguided rocket pods, 12 laser-guided missiles, 23mm gunpods
First flight:	27 July 1982

The Ka50 Werewolf is the world's first single-seat close-support helicopter. Unlike NATO attack helicopters, it does not locate targets itself, but relies on other aircraft to do this before it attacks. The theory behind this is that the helicopter is not so vulnerable to attack itself. Even so, the Werewolf is protected by armour plate that can withstand the impact of 20mm shells and pods on the wingtips carry electronic counter measures packages and flare dispensers. The pilot is protected by a double-walled steel cockpit with bulletproof canopy and has a rocket-powered ejector seat should nhe need to abandon the helicopter. Before the ejector seat is launched, explosive bolts blow off the rotor blades and the cockpit roof. The Werewolf remained something of a mystery in the West for around seven years after its first flight.

LOCKHEED/BOEING F-22A RAPIER

Type:	single-seat air superiority fighter
Engines:	two 15,900kg thrust Pratt and Whitney F119-100 augmented turbofans
Wingspan:	13.11m (43ft)
Length:	19.57m (64ft 2in)
Height:	5.39m (17ft 8in)
Weight:	15,420kg (34,000lb) empty; 28,120kg (62,000lb) normal take-off weight
Maximum speed:	1480km/h (920mph)
Service ceiling:	21,330m (70,000ft)
Maximum range:	1480km (800 miles) combat radius
Armament:	one 20mm cannon, four AIM-120A and four AIM-9 Sidewinder missiles
First flight:	29 September 1990

The F-22A Rapier, jointly produced by Lockheed and Boeing, is intended as the United States' front-line fighter for the next century. The angular design of the airframe incorporates stealth technology, making the Rapier difficult for enemy radar to track. A fly-by-wire flight control system and thrust vectoring exhaust nozzles combine to make this a highly manoeuvrable and agile fighter that can make lightning surprise attacks on its targets. The high performance powerplants give the aircraft 'Supercruise' capability, allowing sustained supersonic flight. Anti-aircraft missiles and precision guided weapons are carried in internal bays in the fuselage. First flight of the production model Rapier should take place in early 1977, with delivery scheduled for 2000.

LOCKHEED F-117A NIGHTHAWK

Type:	single-seat attack and defence suppression aircraft
Engines:	two 4900kg thrust General Electric F404-F1D2 turbofans
Wingspan:	13.20m (43ft 4in)
Length:	20.08m (65ft 11in)
Height:	3.78m (12ft 5in)
Weight:	13,380kg (29,500lb) empty; 23,810kg (52,500lb) maximum take-off weight
Maximum speed:	1040km/h (646mph)
Service ceiling:	not known
Maximum range:	2040km (1100 miles) without refuelling
Armament:	up to 2,300kg (5000lb) bombs and air-to-ground missiles
First flight:	18 June 1981

The Lockheed F-117A Nighthawk, popularly known as the Stealth Fighter, came to international prominence for its role in the Gulf War in 1990-91. Designed to be invisible to radar, the Nighthawk is capable of delivering its ordnance with great accuracy. The fuselage is comprised of flat panels called facets, which reflect radar energy away from the station that transmitted it. In addition, all the surfaces are coated with radar-absorbent materials. Heat absorbing tiles around the engine exhausts minimise the chance of detection by infra-red tracking. Infra-red sensors and laser targetting, used in conjunction with the laser-guided bombs carried in the weapons bay, ensure the accuracy of the Nighthawk's weapons delivery. The Nighthawk can also be equipped with air-to-air missiles.

McDonnell Douglas F-4 Phantom

Type:	multi-role fighter/defence suppression aircraft
Engines:	two 8120kg thrust GE J79-17 afterburning turbojets (F-4E and G)
Wingspan:	11.7m (38ft 5in)
Length:	19.2m (63ft)
Height:	4.95m (16ft 3in)
Weight:	13,400kg (29,535lb) empty; 28,030kg (61,795lb) maximum load (F-4E)
Maximum speed:	2300km/h (1430mph)
Service ceiling:	16,800m (55,000ft)
Maximum range:	930km (500 miles)
Armament:	one 20mm M-61 cannon, four AIM-7 and four AIM-9 missiles (F-4E); four HARM missiles (F-4G)
First flight:	27 May 1958 (prototype)

The McDonnell Douglas F-4 Phantom is one of the classic combat aircraft designs. It has been built in larger numbers than any other warplane since World War Two, a testament to the success of its design. The Phantom was originally intended for the role of carrier-borne attack plane, but its potential was soon exploited as a multi-role fighter for land-based as well as carrier-based deployment. A number of versions of the Phantom were produced, tailored to meet a number of requirements, including reconnaissance, ground attack and air superiority roles, operating from land and sea, deployed by the US Navy, Air Force and Marine Corps. Latterly, the Phantom has found a new lease of life in its 'Wild Weasel' defence suppression role, equipped with specialised equipment for taking out enemy radar stations and ground defences.

McDonnell Douglas F-15 Eagle

Type: air superiority fighter

Engines: two 10,600kg thrust Pratt and Whitney F200-100 afterburning turbofans

Wingspan: 13.05m (42ft 10in)

Length: 19.43m (63ft 9in)

Height: 5.63m (18ft 5in)

Weight: 13,744kg (30,300lb) empty; 30,840kg (68,000lb) maximum take-off weight

Maximum speed: 2655km/h (1665mph)

Service ceiling: 19,800m (65,000ft)

Maximum range: 930km (500 miles) combat radius

Armament: one 20mm M61A cannon, four AIM-7 and four AIM-9 missiles or eight AIM-120 missiles

First flight: February 1979

The McDonnell Douglas F-15 Eagle is an all-weather, extremely manoeuvrable, tactical fighter, designed to gain and maintain air superiority in aerial combat. It was intended to replace the ageing Phantom II. The Eagle's air superiority is achieved through a mixture of manoeuvrability and acceleration. It has electronic systems and weaponry to detect, acquire, track and destroy enemy aircraft and its weapons and flight control systems are designed so one person can safely and effectively perform air-to-air combat. The pilot has an excellent all-round field of vision. The F-15s avionics system has a head-up display, tactical navigation system, instrument landing system and an internally mounted, tactical electronic-warfare system, 'identification friend or foe' system and electronic countermeasures.

F-15E STRIKE EAGLE

Type: dual-role interdictor

Engines: two 10,600kg thrust Pratt and Whitney F200-100 afterburning turbofans

Wingspan: 13.05m (42ft 10in)

Length: 19.43m (63ft 9in)

Height: 5.63m (18ft 5in)

Weight: 14,500kg (32,000lb) empty; 36,740kg (81,000lb) maximum take-off weight

Maximum speed: 2655km/h (1650mph)

Service ceiling: 19,800m (65,000ft)

Maximum range: 1270km (6854 miles) combat radius

Armament: one 20mm M61-A cannon and 10,900kg (24,000lb) maximum external load

First flight: July 1980

Developed from the F-15 Eagle, the F-15E Strike Eagle
is one of the world's finest fighter-bombers. It was
introduced to supplement the United States Air Force's
fleet of F-111 fighter-bombers. The primary mission of
the Strike Eagle is as an air-to-ground strike aircraft and
a wide range of guided and unguided weapons,
including stand-off nuclear bombs, can be carried on its
18 weapons hardpoints for the execution of this role.
For its air superiority role the Strike Eagle can be fitted
with eight anti-aircraft missiles of various types and also
has a six-barrel 20mm cannon. Operational aircraft were
delivered to the USAF in 1988-89 and the Strike Eagle
had a high degree of success during the Gulf War against
Iraq in 1990-91, leading to a number of export orders
from both Israel and Saudi Arabia.

McDONNELL DOUGLAS F/A18 HORNET

Type: single/twin-seat multi-mission strike fighter

Engines: two General Electric F404-400 augmented turbofans

Wingspan: 11.43m (37ft 6in)

Length: 17.07m (56ft)

Height: 4.66m (15ft 3in)

Weight: 10,430kg (23,000lb) empty; 16,770kg (36,970lb) maximum take-off weight

Maximum speed: 1910km/h (1190mph)

Service ceiling: 15,240m (50,000ft)

Maximum range: 1070km (575 miles) on attack mission

Armament: one 20mm M61-A1 multi-barrel cannon plus variety of air-to-air or air-to-ground ordnance depending on mission

First flight: 18 November 1978

The McDonnell Douglas F/A-18 Hornet was designed as a carrier-based fighter and attack aircraft to replace both the Phantom II and A-7 Corsair. Initially the intention had been to have two new aircraft but it was realised that one could play both roles effectively, by simply reprogramming its computer software. F/A-18A, the fighter version, is a single-seat aircraft, whereas the F/A-18B attack craft is a twin-seat aircraft. The Hornet has been deployed to both the US Navy and Marine Corps and can be equipped for anti-ship and anti-submarine engagements, as well as ground attack missions with guided bombs. Electronic counter measures pods can be fitted to one or two of the aircraft's nine external hardpoints, along with the weaponry needed for the execution of the mission.

McDonnell Douglas Apache

Type:	attack helicopter
Engines:	two General Electric GE T700-701 free-turbine turboshafts
Rotor diameter:	14.63m (48ft)
Length:	17.76m (58ft 3in)
Height:	3.84m (16ft 9in)
Weight:	5060kg (11,150lb) empty; 8000kg (17,650lb) maximum loaded
Maximum speed:	365 km/h (230mph)
Service ceiling:	6400m (21,000ft)
Maximum range:	480km (260 miles) on internal fuel
Armament:	one Hughes M23-A1 30mm Chain Gun, four Hellfire missiles or 76 70mm rockets in four pods
First flight:	30 September 1975

The McDonnell Douglas Apache is a first-rate attack helicopter. The pilot is equipped with a forward-looking infra-red sensor that provides him with a thermal image of the terrain ahead, allowing him to fly low-level missions at night or in bad weather. Once the target has been located, the laser tracker and rangefinder of the target acquisition system allows the co-pilot to lock on the weapons systems, including the powerful Hellfire anti-tank guided missile. The two-man crew are heavily protected from counter-attack by armoured shields that can withstand the impact of 12.7mm calibre ammunition and the Black Hole infra-red suppression system protects the Apache from heat-seeking missiles. If the worst happens, and the helicopter is shot down, the airframe is rugged enough to survive crashes at up to 45km/h (30mph).

MD500 DEFENDER

Type:	light military helicopter
Engines:	Allison 250-C20B turboshaft
Rotor diameter:	not available
Length:	7.29m (23ft 11in)
Height:	2.62m (8ft 7in)
Weight:	898kg (1979lb) empty, equipped; 1400kg (3100lb) maximum take-off weight
Maximum speed:	241km/h (150mph)
Service ceiling:	4875m (16,000ft)
Maximum range:	478km (300 miles)
Armament:	machine-gun pods, rocket launchers, Stinger anti-aircraft missiles, anti tank missiles
First flight:	27 February 1963

The McDonnell Douglas Defender is one of the world's foremost light military helicopters. It was developed from an earlier helicopter design, the Hughes 500, that was originally produced for civilian purposes. The Defender comes in a number of variants tailored to perform a range of military duties. Although fairly small, the Defender can carry a considerable amount of ordnance and packs a powerful punch. The United States Army Special Forces use specially configured Defenders to land troops behind enemy lines and for intelligence gathering and command purposes. Naval versions of the Defender are kitted out for anti-submarine warfare, carrying magnetic anomaly detectors to find their target and torpedoes to attack it. The Defender can also be used as an anti-tank helicopter.

MiG-23 Flogger

Type:	single seat air combat fighter
Engines:	Soyuz/Khachaturov R35-300 turbojet
Wingspan:	13.96m (45ft 10in) spread; 7.78m (25ft 6in) swept
Length:	16.71m (54ft 10in)
Height:	4.82m (15ft 10in)
Weight:	10,200kg (22,485lb) empty; 17,800kg (39,250lb) maximum take-off weight
Maximum speed:	2500km/h (1553mph)
Service ceiling:	18,500m (60,700ft)
Maximum range:	2820km (1750 miles) with external fuel tanks
Armament:	23mm twin-barrelled gun, plus varied missile packages carried on underwing pylons
First flight:	10 June 1967 (prototype)

Designated 'Flogger' by the NATO forces, the MiG-23 first entered service in the early 1970s. It continued to be produced in fairly large numbers up until the late 1980s and is still in service with many of the former Warsaw Pact allies of the old Soviet Union. It was developed from the classic MiG-21 design, which had been the mainstay of the Soviet and Warsaw Pact air forces in the 1960s. The MiG-23 departed drastically from the older aircraft in having swingwings. Along with the Sukhoi Su-17, it was one of the first Russian-designed aircraft to feature this new development in aircraft design. Several models of the MiG-23 went into service, differing in engine type, four different engines were used, and in other capabilities. A two-seater trainer, the Flogger-C, which was capable of going into combat, was among those produced.

MiG-25

Type:	single-seat interceptor/reconnaissance
Engines:	two Tumnasky R15BD-300 turbojets
Wingspan:	14.01m (46ft)
Length:	23.82m (78ft 2in)
Height:	6.1m (20ft)
Weight:	36,720kg (80,950lb) fully loaded (maximum internal fuel and four missiles)
Maximum speed:	3000km/h (1865mph)
Service ceiling:	20,700m (67,900ft)
Maximum range:	1250km (776 miles) at supersonic speeds
Armament:	four air-to-air missiles carried on underwing pylons
First flight:	9 September 1964 (prototype)

The MiG-25 was produced as an answer to a threat that never really got off the ground. Soviet intelligence learned of the American Valkyrie superbomber with a planned top speed of Mach 3. The Valkyrie never saw service, but the fighter that was intended to intercept it did. The first prototype of the MiG-25 interceptor took to the air on 9 September 1964. Its high set wings, large air intakes for the powerful turbojets and twin outward-leaning tailplanes are distinctive. Several models were produced for a variety of tasks. These include the MiG-25RB, a reconnaissance plane that can also carry out bombing missions, and the MiG-25BM, designed to take out enemy surface-to-air missile sites. The interceptor model, the MiG-25PD, carries four air-to-air missiles in underwing racks.

MiG-27

Type:	single-seat ground-attack aircraft
Engines:	Soyuz/Khachaturov R29B-300 turbojet
Wingspan:	13.96m (45ft 10in) spread; 7.78m (25ft 6in) swept
Length:	17.08m (56ft)
Height:	5m (16ft 5in)
Weight:	11,908kg (26,252lb) empty; 20,670kg (45,570lb) maximum take-off weight
Maximum speed:	1885km/h (1170mph)
Service ceiling:	14,000m (45,900ft)
Maximum range:	540km (335 miles) with external tanks
Armament:	one 23mm twin-barrel gun; 4000kg of assorted weaponry on external pylons (including tactical nuclear bombs)
First flight:	entered service late 1970s

The MiG-27 strike aircraft grew out of improvements
that were made to the design of the MiG-23. It was
originally developed in the 1970s to give ground-attack
support to Warsaw Pact troops. Full-scale production and
active service duties for the MiG-27 began in the late
1970s. Although broadly similar in appearance to the
MiG-23, the MiG-27 is a slightly longer and somewhat
heavier aircraft with a sophisticated electronic
navigational-attack system that allows the pilot to put the
aircraft on autopilot and navigate to the target at night or
in adverse weather. A laser rangefinder helps ensure the
accuracy of the attack. Several variants of the MiG-27D,
the basic attack model, were produced, each representing
an upgrading of one system or another. Work on new
models ceased in the mid-1980s.

MiG-29 Fulcrum

Type:	single-seat counter-air fighter
Engines:	two Klimov/Sarkisov R17-33 turbofans
Wingspan:	11.36m (37ft 3in)
Length:	17.32m (56ft 10in)
Height:	4.73m (15ft 6in)
Weight:	10,900kg (24,030lb) empty; 18,500kg (40,785lb) maximum take-off weight
Maximum speed:	2445km/h (1520mph)
Service ceiling:	17,000m (55,775ft)
Maximum range:	2900km (1800 miles) with external tanks
Armament:	one 30mm GSh-301 gun and six close-range air-to-air missiles, or four close range and two medium range radar guided missiles
First flight:	6 October 1977

The MiG-29, codenamed Fulcrum by NATO, was designed to be a replacement for a number of ageing aircraft designs in the Soviet forces, including the Sukhoi Su-15 and Su-17 counter-air and attack craft and the MiG-21 and MiG-23 fighter aircraft. Entering service in 1984, the MiG-29 proved to be a highly manoeuvrable and capable aircraft. Broadly similar to the McDonnell Douglas F-15 in appearance, although significantly smaller in size, the MiG-29 is one of the world's finest combat aircraft. The original Fulcrum-A was delivered in three basic forms, and there have been a few variants on the basic design since, including a proposed carrier-based version that was eventually rejected in favour of the Sukhoi Su-27, and a combat-capable, two-seater training aircraft.

MiG-31

Type:	long-range interceptor
Engines:	two Aviadvigatel D-30F6 afterburning turbofans
Wingspan:	13.46m (44ft 2in)
Length:	22.69m (74ft 5in)
Height:	6.15m (20ft 2in)
Weight:	21,825kg (48,115lb) empty; 46,200kg (101,850lb) maximum take-off weight
Maximum speed:	3000km/h (1865mph)
Service ceiling:	20,600m (67,600ft)
Maximum range:	3300km (2050 miles) with external tanks
Armament:	one 23mm six-barrel gun, assortment of air-to-air missiles
First flight:	16 September 1975 (prototype)

The MiG-31 long-range interceptor was designed to counter the threat from American Cruise missiles and from high-speed, low-level attack aircraft. The prototype for the MiG-31 was a converted MiG-25 and the MiG-31 is similar in general appearance to that aircraft. The MiG-31 is a very different aircraft in many repects, however. It has a specially strengthened airframe that allows it to withstand the stresses of sustained low-altitude supersonic flight and is equipped with more powerful twin turbofan engines. Its fire-control radar system is capable of tracking ten objects simultaneously and targetting four of them. Responsibility for this sophisticated equipment and the array of weapons available belongs to the weapons station officer, who sits behind the pilot.

MIL MI-28 HAVOC

Type:	attack helicopter
Engines:	two Isotov TV3-117 turboshafts
Rotor diameter:	17.2m (56ft 5in)
Length:	16.85m (55ft 3in)
Height:	4.81m (15ft 9in)
Weight:	7000kg (15,430lb) empty; 10,400kg (22,900lb) maximum take-off weight
Maximum speed:	300km/h (186mph)
Service ceiling:	not known
Maximum range:	not known
Armament:	30mm cannon, 16 anti-tank missiles, four 20 x 55mm rocket launchers, or four anti-aircraft missiles, or a combination of these
First flight:	November 1982

The Mil Mi-28 attack helicopter, codenamed Havoc by NATO, is intended to enter service with the Russian forces in the late 1990s. Developed from earlier models in the Mil series, the Havoc owes more to the design of a typical American helicopter, particularly the McDonnell Douglas Apache. It has a slimmer fuselage than its predecessors and is highly manoeuvrable, able to take on other helicopters in air-to-air combat, as well as performing its other role as an anti-tank attack helicopter. The crew are protected by titanium steel armour, infra-red suppression technology that hides the tell-tale engine exhaust and infra-red decoys protect the Havoc from heat-seeking missiles. A second version of the Mi-28, the Havoc-B, which will be equipped for night flying and finding its target in adverse weather, is also being developed.

MITSUBISHI FS-X

Type: single-seat fighter-bomber

Engines: one General Electric FII0-GE-129 afterburning turbofan

Wingspan: 11.13m (36ft 6in)

Length: 15.27m (50ft 1in)

Height: 4.97m (16ft 3in)

Weight: 9525kg (21,000lb) empty; 22,100kg (48,700lb) maximum take-off weight

Maximum speed: not known

Service ceiling: not known

Maximum range: not known

Armament: 20mm multi-barrel cannon, five hard-points for anti-aircraft missiles

First flight: 12 January 1995

The Mitsubishi FS-X is to be the Japanese Air Self-Defence Force's frontline fighter-bomber for the next century. Currently undergoing extensive trialling, it is expected to enter service some time in the next century, although escalating production costs have placed the schedule in some jeopardy. It is based on the Lockheed F-16 Fighting Falcon, an aircraft that it greatly resembles in appearance. Differences include a Japanese designed wing that is greater in span and area than that of the Fighting Falcon and a longer forward fuselage to accommodate the improved radar system and other avionics. The cockpit features state-of-the-art electronic displays, including a holographic display. Trialling of the four prototypes that have been constructed should run up until the end of this century.

PANAVIA TORNADO ADV

Type: air defence and air superiority fighter

Engines: two Turbo-Union RB199-34R
                       afterburning turbofans

Wingspan: 8.60m (28ft 2in) fully swept; 13.91m
                       (45ft 7in) fully spread

Length: 18.68m (61ft 3in)

Height: 5.95m (19ft 6in)

Weight: 14,500kg (31,800lb) empty; 28,000kg
                       (61,700lb) maximum take-off weight

Maximum speed: 2338km/h (1453mph)

Service ceiling: 21,335m (70,000ft)

Maximum range: 1850km (1150 miles) subsonic
                       intercept radius

Armament: one 27mm cannon, four Skyflash and
                       four Sidewinder air-to-air missiles

First flight: 27 October 1979

The Panavia Tornado IDS, known in the RAF as the Tornado GR.Mk1, was produced as a joint venture between the governments of Germany, Italy and Great Britain. The Tornado ADV was developed from this aircraft by the RAF as a successor to its Phantoms and Lightnings in the air defence and air superiority aspects of the defence of Britain. It was also intended to provide long-range defensive cover for British naval forces. The fuselage of the ADV is longer than that of the IDS, having been extended to provide space for pairs of anti-aircraft missiles beneath the fuselage. Underwing pylons allow further missiles to be loaded. The ADV is also equipped with the sophisticated Foxhunter radar system that can track several targets simultaneously at a distance of over 180km.

ROCKWELL OV-10 BRONCO

Type:	battlefield reconnaissance and counter insurgency
Engines:	two Garrett T76-G-416 turboprops
Wingspan:	12.19m (40ft)
Length:	12.67m (41ft 7in)
Height:	4.62m (15ft 2in)
Weight:	4494kg (9900lb) empty; 6550kg (14,444lb) maximum take-off weight
Maximum speed:	452km/h (281mph)
Service ceiling:	7300m (24,000ft)
Maximum range:	1400km (1200 miles)
Armament:	four 0.3in machine-guns, 1600kg of stores, including anti-aircraft missiles, cluster bombs, rocket launchers and cannon pods
First flight:	July 1965

The Rockwell OV-10 Bronco had its origins in the Vietnam War, entering service in 1967. It took on the role of forward air control, locating, identifying and marking Viet Cong targets, which were then attacked by tactical aircraft. The cockpit is positioned to give a superb field of view. The Bronco also performed well in its other duties as helicopter escort, battlefield reconnaissance and light attack aircraft. Now reduced to a token presence in the United States Air Force, the Bronco continues to play an important part in the US Marine Corps, especially in the shape of its OV-10D night observation and surveillance aircraft, which has been equipped with more powerful engines. Several variations have been produced for export to other countries, including the OV-10B, produced as an unarmed target-towing tug for Germany.

SAAB DRAKEN

Type:	single-seat interceptor
Engines:	one Volvo Flygmotor RM6C afterburning turbojet
Wingspan:	9.42m (30ft 11in)
Length:	15.34m (50ft 5in)
Height:	3.89m (12ft 9in)
Weight:	12,500kg (27,557lb) maximum take-off weight
Maximum speed:	2126km/h (1321mph)
Service ceiling:	15,000m (49,340ft)
Maximum range:	2750km (1710 miles)
Armament:	one 30mm cannon and six missiles, combination of Sidewinders and Falcons
First flight:	March 1960

The Saab Draken had a futuristic appearance when the prototype first flew over 40 years ago and even today its sleek double-delta profile is quite unmistakable. It first entered service with the Swedish Air Force in March 1960 and from that time a number of improvements kept the Draken at the forefront of fighter development. Twin tail wheels were introduced to give aerodynamic braking on landing, allowing the Draken to use shortened or damaged airfields. Further improvements included upgraded radar incorporated in the J35E reconnaissance variant, and the J35F air defence variant, equipped with homing anti-aircraft missiles. Few Drakens now remain in active service with the Swedish forces, as they have been largely superseded by the Viggen and Gripen, but many still fly with other air forces.

SAAB VIGGEN

Type: ground attack and strike aircraft

Engines: Volvo Flygmotor RM8A afterburning turbofan

Wingspan: 10.6m (34ft 9in)

Length: 16.3m (53ft 6in)

Height: 5.6m (18ft 4in)

Weight: 12,250kg (27,000lb) empty; 17,000kg (37,500lb) normal take-off weight

Maximum speed: 2124km/h (1320mph)

Service ceiling: 18,290m (60,000ft)

Maximum range: 2000km (1250 miles)

Armament: 6000kg of assorted ordnance, including a variety of air-to-air missiles, rocket pods and gun pods

First flight: 21 June 1971 (entered service)

The Saab Viggen, developed for the Swedish air force in
the 1960s, was the first fast jet to feature a pair of
forewings in addition to the main delta wings. The
forewings, called canards, allow the aircraft to fly low and
slow while maintaining stability. They also give the
Viggen the ability to take off in a short distance, allowing
it to operate from motorways in an emergency. The first
version of the Viggen was the AJ37 attack fighter,
capable of being deployed against targets on land and
sea. The most recent version, the JA37 is primarily an
interceptor but it can also be used for ground attack. The
JA37 has improved flight stability over earlier models
and produces more thrust from its turbine and
combustion burner system. Like the Draken, the Viggen
is being replaced by the new Gripen and the JA37 will be
the last model produced.

SAAB GRIPEN

Type:	single-seat multi-role fighter
Engines:	one General Electric/Volvo Flygmotor RM12 afterburning turbofan
Wingspan:	8.4m (27ft 7in)
Length:	14.1m (46ft 3in)
Height:	4.5m (14ft 9in)
Weight:	6620kg (14,600lb) empty; 12,500kg (27,560lb) maximum take-off weight
Maximum speed:	2126km/h (1320mph)
Service ceiling:	not known
Maximum range:	not known
Armament:	one 27mm cannon, 6500kg of assorted ordnance, including air-to-surface rockets, air-to-air missiles, freefall bombs and sensor pods
First flight:	8 December 1988

The Saab JAS39 Gripen is the world's first lightweight multi-role combat aircraft. The letters JAS come from the Swedish for Fighter, Attack and Reconnaissance, as the Gripen is designed to perform all three of these missions. It was commissioned by the Swedish government as a replacement for the Saab Viggen and Draken. The Gripen is easily adapted to each of its three roles by reprogramming its onboard electronic systems. A fly-by-wire control system and movable forewings, combined with a sleek delta wing make the Gripen a highly manoeuvrable aircraft. A number of multi-function displays are available for the pilot, including all the target data gathered from radar, weapons sensors and a front-looking infra-red system. The 'programmable' Gripen will be able to adapt to the changing demands placed on a fighter aircraft well into the 21st century.

SEPECAT JAGUAR

Type:	single-seat attack aircraft
Engines:	two Rolls-Royce Turbomeca Adour Mk 104 turbofans
Wingspan:	8.69m (28ft 6in)
Length:	16.83m (55ft 2in)
Height:	4.89m (16ft)
Weight:	10,955kg (24,150lb) empty; 15,700kg (34,610lb) maximum take-off weight
Maximum speed:	1700km/h (1056mph)
Service ceiling:	14,000m (46,000ft)
Maximum range:	not available
Armament:	two 30mm cannon, 4800kg of disposable stores, including anti-aircraft missiles, anti-radar missiles, guided bombs, cluster bombs and rocket launchers
First flight:	September 1968

The SEPECAT Jaguar is a prime example of cooperation between two nations to produce a first-class aircraft. In the 1960s Britain and France, working separately to develop a single-seat attack plane and a two-seat trainer, saw the advantages in combining their efforts to produce a single aircraft type with variants to suit their respective requirements. Starting from the French design specifications, the aircraft was equipped with powerful turbofans, giving a short take-off capability. After first flights in September 1968, the Jaguar A single-seat attack and Jaguar E two-seat trainer were developed for the French air force. The RAF equivalents were the Jaguar GR Mk1 and Jaguar T.Mk2. The Jaguar GR.Mk1A, which saw service in the Gulf War against Iraq, was equipped with an improved navigational/attack system.

SUKHOI SU-27 FLANKER

Type: interceptor fighter

Engines: two Lyul'ka AL-31F turbofans

Wingspan: 14.7m (48ft 2in)

Length: 21.9m (72ft)

Height: 5.93m (18ft 5in)

Weight: 22,000kg (45,800lb) empty; 30,000kg
                       (66,130lb) maximum take-off weight

Maximum speed: 2500km/h (1550mph)

Service ceiling: 18,000m (59,000ft)

Maximum range: 4000km (2485 miles)

Armament: one 30mm cannon, 6000kg of
                       ordnance, including air-to-air missiles,
                       rocket launchers, freefall bombs, drop
                       tanks and electronic counter
                       measures pods

First flight: 20 May 1977

The Sukhoi Su-27, codenamed Flanker by NATO, entered service in 1984. Its sophisticated fly-by-wire control system, radar target acquisition and array of 10 air-to-air missiles made it a formidable opponent. Missile launch rails were added to the wingtips of the Flanker-B. A twin-seat model of the Su-27, the Flanker-C, was produced in 1989, performing dual roles as both trainer and combat aircraft. In combat mode, the rear seat is occupied by the weapons officer, who also looks after the aircraft's electronic navigation systems. The Su-27K won out over the MiG-29K as the Russians' carrier-based aircraft of choice and was deployed in 1992. It was modified for its naval role by the addition of folding wings and tailplanes, strengthened landing gear, an arrestor hook, and a retractable in-flight refuelling probe.

SUKHOI SU-35 FLANKER

Type: interceptor fighter

Engines: two Lyul'ka AL-31F turbofans

Wingspan: 14.7m (48ft 2in)

Length: 21.9m (72ft)

Height: 5.93m (18ft 5in)

Weight: 22,000kg (45,800lb) empty; 30,000kg (66,130lb) maximum take-off weight

Maximum speed: 2500km/h (1550mph)

Service ceiling: 18,000m (59,000ft)

Maximum range: 1500km (930 miles) combat radius

Armament: one 30mm cannon, 6000kg of ordnance, including air-to-air missiles, rocket launchers, freefall bombs, drop tanks and electronic counter measures pods

First flight: 1994

The Sukhoi Su-35 is a direct development of the Su-27 and is also codenamed Flanker by NATO. The most important improvement in this new model is the ability to control the direction of the engine thrust, called thrust vector control, which is operated via the aircraft's digital flight control system. This dramatically increases the manoeuvrability of the aircraft. In addition, a complex array of forward and rear-facing radar detection sytems and a sensor mounted on top of the fuselage will make the Su-35 a difficult target to take on. It is also well equipped to take offensive action, with the ability to carry 6000kg of assorted munitions, including air-to-air missiles and rocket launchers. Lack of funding may delay the active service appearance of this latest addition to the Russian air force.

WESTLAND LYNX

Type: Army/Navy multi-role helicopter
(statistics are for Navy version)

Engines: two Rolls-Royce Gem 41-2 turboshafts

Rotor diameter: 12.8m (42ft)

Length: 15.16m (49ft 9in)

Height: 3.48m (11ft 5in)

Weight: 3340kg (7370lb) empty, 4760kg
(10,500lb) maximum take-off weight

Maximum speed: 232km/h (144mph)

Hovering ceiling: 2575m (8450ft)

Maximum range: 1300km (834 miles)

Armament: 0.5in machine-gun pod, homing
torpedoes, semi-active homing
missiles, depth charges

First flight: 12 April 1972 (Army prototype)

The Westland Lynx was produced primarily to answer the Royal Navy's need for a new shipborne helicopter, although the first production model to enter service was the Army model, the AH-1 general purpose battlefield helicopter. The first naval production model was the Lynx HAS-2, which differed from the Army model in having fixed-wheel landing gear rather than skids. The Army model carries out transport and anti-tank duties, while the Navy Lynx can be equipped for anti-submarine search-and-kill, reconnaissance, sea-air rescue and transport roles. A number of variants have been produced to deal with different operating conditions, such as the HAS.3GM, with improved cooling systems for places such as the Gulf, and the HAS.3ICE, which flies from the Antarctic survey vessel HMS Endurance.

GLOSSARY

Here are a few combat aviation terms you may come across.

AAM: anti-aircraft missile.

afterburner: burns fuel in the jet pipe to give a short burst of increased thrust.

AGM: air-to-ground missile.

ALARM: Air Launched Anti-Radiation Missile.

ALCM: Air Launched Cruise Missile.

ARM: anti-radiation missile, which homes in on radar.

ATGM: anti-tank guided missile.

avionics: aviation electronics.

AWACS: airborne warning and control system.

canopy: the transparent cockpit cover.

COINS: computer operated instrument system.

combat radius: the distance an aircraft can fly from its base to engage an enemy and then return to the same base again.

comm/nav: communications and navigation.

CP/G: co-pilot/gunner.

ECM: electronic counter measures.

external stores: anything carried outside the aircraft fuselage, such as drop tanks and missiles.

FLIR: forward looking infrared, a target seeking system.

fly-by-wire: flight surfaces which are controlled electronically rather than manually.

hardpoints: pylons and other fittings which are used for the attachment of missiles and other loads on the outside of the aircraft.

HUD: head-up display, which projects instrument read outs onto the pilot's helmet visor.

HUDWAC: head-up display weapons

aiming computer.

INS: inertial navigation system.

knot: 1 nautical mile per hour.

LANTIRN: low altitude navigation and targetting, infra-red, night.

Loran: long-range navigation.

Mach number: a fraction or multiple of the speed of sound. Mach 1, the speed of sound, is 1220km/h (760mph).

MAD: magnetic anomaly detector, which is used to detect submarines underwater.

MTOW: maximum take-off weight.

optronics: combined optical and electronic sighting systems.

payload: the cargo which is carried by an aircraft that is necessary for the completion of its mission, this could be, for example, extra fuel tanks, bombs and missiles.

RWR: radar warning receiver, which alerts pilots to the fact that they are being tracked by enemy radar.

SAM: surface-to-air missile.

SAR: search and rescue.

service ceiling: the height at which an aircraft's maximum rate of climb is 30.48m (100ft) per second.

sigint: signals intelligence.

signature: the characteristic infra-red,

radar and other electromagnetic radiation given off by an aircraft that can be used to identify it from a distance.

SRAM: short-range attack missile.

STOL: short take-off and landing.

stores: any objects carried outside the aircraft attached to the hardpoints or pylons.

turbofan: a gas turbine engine in which a fan is used to generate thrust.

turbojet: a gas turbine engine in which the thrust is delivered by expelling the exhaust gases.

turboprop: a gas turbine that is used to drive an aircraft's propeller.

usable fuel: the fuel carried by the aircraft that can actually be used in flight, generally about 95% of the total capacity of the tanks.

useful load: the carrying capacity of the aircraft plus its usable fuel load.

V/STOL: vertical/short take-off and landing.

VTOL: vertical take-off and landing.